The Day Martin Luther King Jr. Died

Veronica Enix
Illustrated by Taylor Bruce

The Day Martin Luther King Jr. Died
©1997 Wright Group Publishing, Inc.
©1997 Veronica Enix
Illustrated by Taylor Bruce

Story Vine™
© Wright Group Publishing, Inc.

The Wright Group
19201 120th Avenue NE
Bothell, WA 98011

Printed in Canada

10 9 8 7 6 5 4

ISBN: 0-7802-8320-1

I dedicate this book to the students at Budlong Elementary School in Los Angeles, who taught me that it is important to allow for individual differences in order to make a difference in an individual's life.
I also dedicate this book to Raymond G. Enix, my husband and my best friend, who continually encourages me to live my dreams.

I remember that day in April 1968. It was just another Thursday—at first. I was in the third grade at a school on Chicago's South Side. I had stayed late for the after-school study program.

Some kids were working on their homework while others were being tutored in math. But we were really all waiting to play musical chairs. Mrs. Lewis, the teacher in charge, had promised we could play that game before we went home.

I was staring at a bulletin board that showed bread, milk, fruit and vegetables, and meat below a sign that read, "You Are What You Eat." I was wondering what Mama would make us for dinner that night.

Finally, Mrs. Lewis got up from her chair and announced, "Boys and girls, it's time for our game now. Please put everything away." We did as she asked.

Mrs. Lewis continued. "I need helpers to set up chairs for the game. Who would like to help?" She chose four volunteers, who hurried to carry chairs to the front of the room.

All of a sudden the door banged open, and the teacher from next door, Mrs. Ray, ran into our room. She had an expression of fear on her face that I'd never seen before.

"Paula, did you hear? Did you hear?" she shouted.

"Did I hear what?" Mrs. Lewis said as she rushed over to Mrs. Ray.

"They shot him! They shot King!" Mrs. Ray cried.

"Oh, God, no!" Mrs. Lewis exclaimed as she covered her face with her hands. Then she said in a quiet, serious voice, "Boys and girls, please sit down and stay in your seats."

The two teachers left the room.

Some kids in the back of the room started playing around. A few kids asked, "Who is this King?"

Soon Mrs. Lewis came back with a television on a tall stand. She rolled it in front of the class, and then she faced us. She was holding back tears. She said, "Class, something terrible has happened. Someone has shot Dr. Martin Luther King."

"Who is he?" asked Kathy.

"I know who King is," said Joseph proudly. "He's the man leading all those marches. Our pastor talks about him all the time at church."

"My mother said that some white people bombed his house one time," Kevin said.

Mrs. Lewis held up her hand for silence. "Dr. King is a very important leader to all black people," she said. "He's a preacher from the state of Georgia. He works for equal rights for all people."

5

Some of the kids were asking questions, but Mrs. Lewis said, "Hush, children." She turned the television on. "We can find out more about this on TV."

A news reporter began by saying, "We interrupt this program to bring you a special bulletin. Today in Memphis, Tennessee, Dr. Martin Luther King Jr. was shot on his hotel balcony. He was in Memphis in support of a strike by city sanitation workers. Police report that the gunman responsible for the shooting is still at large. No further information is available at this time."

The news report ended.

"But is he alive? Is he still alive?" Mrs. Lewis asked softly, as tears ran down her cheeks.

Then we heard the voice of the head teacher over the intercom. "Your attention, please," said Mr. Wimberfield. "We have received news that Martin Luther King Jr. was shot today in Memphis, Tennessee. We do not know the extent of his injuries at this time. This comes as shocking news to us all. We are deeply saddened by this act. As we prepare to leave this evening, let's remember, boys and girls, to go straight home. Teachers, please remind your group at dismissal. Thank you."

Mrs. Lewis reminded us to finish our schoolwork at home. "But I want you to do one other thing," she said. "I want each of you to ask your parents, your grandparents, and your friends about Dr. Martin Luther King Jr. Find out who he is, what he's done, and what he stands for. He is…"

7

Mrs. Lewis started to cry again. She was always a strong person, always in control of everything. She kept her face in her hands. We watched her as her shoulders shook. Some of the kids whispered about what was going on. I felt bad about Mrs. Lewis. I wished I could help her stop crying.

When the bell finally rang, Mrs. Lewis said, "Line up, boys and girls. Remember to go straight home." Now her face looked tired.

We all hurried to get in line. The extra chairs for musical chairs were sprawled across the front of the room around the TV stand. Our class-room was usually neat at the end of the day, but today it was a wreck.

As we left the classroom, I wondered if Mrs. Lewis would be OK and if those chairs would still be there tomorrow.

Outside the school, I waited for my brother, Terry. He was in fifth grade. When his class came out, he said, "Hey, Ronnie, want to race?" (Everyone called me "Ronnie," which is short for Veronica.) I was still worried about Mrs. Lewis, but I couldn't resist the challenge of racing Terry home.

When we got to our apartment building, we went inside and waited for the elevator. Some grown-ups were waiting for the elevator, too. They looked sad and serious. Some of them looked angry.

"It just doesn't make any sense," said one woman. "It's just not fair."

The elevator came, and everyone got on. No one said anything from the time we got on until we got off at our floor.

Terry unlocked our door with his key.

I said to him, "You know somebody shot King, don't you?"

"Yeah, I know," said my brother. "But he might be OK. Just wait till Mama finds out."

Terry and I knew that the shooting of Dr. King was serious. But we started to play what we always played after school. We pretended we were cowboys in the Wild West.

"Bang, bang, I gotcha," Terry yelled as he ran past on his pillow-horse.

I grabbed my pillow-horse, dropped to my hands and knees, and pretended my horse and I were shot. I fell to the ground, dead.

Then I got back up. "OK," I said, "now I'm the sheriff, and I get to chase you out of town."

"No," Terry said.

"Why not?" I asked. "Girls can be sheriffs."

"Because you're only eight years old and I'm ten and a half!" Terry laughed and tried to grab my pillow. "I'm the sheriff around here!"

We started to argue, but then we heard Mama's key unlocking the door. Terry grabbed our pillows and threw them on the beds. He straightened up his clothes and walked to the living room looking serious. I did the same.

Whenever Mama came home from work, she put her purse on the table, gave us a hug and a kiss, and asked about our homework. But that night was different.

She walked straight to the television and started turning the channels. "Ronnie," she said, "bring me the telephone."

I ran to the phone on the desk and brought it to her. She sat down with it on her lap, never taking her eyes off the television.

I looked at her sitting there. Who was this teary-eyed, angry woman? She didn't seem like my mama. My mama taught me to be slow to anger. My mama taught me to love, and I could see hate in this woman's eyes. My mama taught me about joy and happiness, but this woman was filled with sadness and sorrow.

The telephone rang, and Mama answered it. "Hello," she said in almost a whisper. "What channel?"

Mama switched channels quickly to a news report. Terry and I joined her on the couch, one of us on each side. A photograph of Dr. King came on the screen as the reporter made his announcement.

Dr. King was dead.

Mama began to sob. "They killed him! Lord have mercy, they killed him!"

Terry hugged Mama as she wept. I had never seen my mother cry before. I could only stare at her. The agony on her face told me that there was bitterness mixed with pain.

"Don't cry, Mama," I said. "Everything is going to be all right."

"No, Honey," she said. "I really don't think so."

I couldn't believe my ears. Mama always told me that everything will turn out for the best. She taught me never to give up hope. But now she seemed hopeless herself.

My mother, my brother, and I sat together on the couch watching the TV. They were showing black people and white people holding hands and singing together:

We shall overcome.
We shall overcome.
We shall overcome someday.
Oh, deep in my heart,
I do believe
We shall overcome someday.

Mama clicked off the TV. "I really should start dinner," she said as she wiped the tears from her eyes. "And you need to start on your homework."

"Mama, why was Dr. King so important?" I asked.

"Oh, Honey," she sighed. "Where do I start? You two come out to the kitchen and help me get dinner ready."

Mama handed me some carrots to wash. She started peeling potatoes and began to talk. "There was a time when blacks had to sit in the back of the bus, or stand up to give white people their seats. Do you remember me telling you that?"

I nodded.

"Thanks to Rosa Parks and Dr. King, we can sit where we want on the bus now," Terry added. "And Dr. King stood for nonviolence."

"That's right," Mama said. "He believed that guns and fighting would never change the prejudices of America."

Mama began cutting up the carrots and potatoes. "Dr. King felt that people had to change what they felt in their hearts. He believed that something happens to a man on the inside when he continues to beat up on peaceful demonstrators marching for equal rights. King believed that nonviolence would spread, and that was how things should change, not by shooting or killing or war."

"I know where he got his ideas," said Terry. "My social studies teacher talks about Dr. Martin Luther King Jr. all the time. He says Dr. King learned about loving your neighbor from Christianity, and he learned about methods of peaceful protest from Mahatma Gandhi of India."

"He also received the Nobel Peace Prize for his nonviolent approach," Mama said. "And that's a great honor."

She put the vegetables on the stove to cook. "Hand me that big skillet now," she said. She got out some leftover meat and gravy to heat up, and she turned to me with a wooden spoon in her hand. "Stir this meat while it heats." She opened the cupboard to get out the plates, and she handed them to Terry.

Then she looked at both of us. "You know what else Dr. King said?

He said that every person should be the best that he or she can be."

"I know, Mama," I said. "If you're a janitor, be the best janitor there is. If you're a doctor, be the best doctor there is. You always tell us that."

Then Mama said something that I will never forget. She said, "The one thing I'll always remember about Martin Luther King is that he wanted justice for *all* people. His death isn't just a loss for black America. It's a loss for all America."

Dinner was ready. After we ate, I finished my homework. In my school notebook, I wrote down everything I had learned about Martin Luther King. I wanted to remember what Mama and Terry said so I could tell Mrs. Lewis and the other kids.

The next morning when I got up, Mama was sitting at the table drinking her tea. "Good morning, Ronnie," she said. Her eyes were red, and the newspaper was spread out on the table.

"Mama, you're not dressed for work," I said. "Are you sick?"

"No," she said. "But I'm not going to work today, and you and your brother aren't going to school."

"Why not?" I asked.

"Because there are riots all over the city. I'll have to go back to work tomorrow. But I don't know just when you and Terry will be going back to school. There are a lot of hurt and angry people out there."

Mama did go back to work the next day. She kept Terry and me out of school for over a week. We weren't allowed to go outside for any reason. The streets looked empty.

During that time, I watched some of Dr. King's famous speeches on television. I began to wonder how Mrs. Lewis felt now and if the chairs were still scattered around the front of the classroom. I wondered if things would ever be the same as before.

Most of all, I wondered about Dr. Martin Luther King Jr. I thought about his famous speech in Washington, D.C., and I remembered how he had ended that speech.

Free at last! Free at last!
Thank God Almighty, we are free at last!

That was what Dr. King believed in. He wished that all of us could join hands together in peace. And then we would all be free.

FROM THE AUTHOR...

Dear Reader,

I was born and raised in Chicago in the early sixties. I believe that writing from experiences is fun and easy. One only has to retell the story or event. I feel that it's important to write down memories, because they make the best stories. I wrote about this memory because it left such an impression on my mind. Throughout my school years I learned a lot about Dr. King. Every time a lesson was taught about him, my mind would reflect on the day he died. I always had strong images of the sad and distressed faces I passed that day.

In college, I became more and more interested in Dr. King and his accomplishments. I began reading his books and truly learned about what he stood for. I remember him now for his great contributions and love of humanity, and I want to share this knowledge with children everywhere. Dr. King is my hero and favorite author.

I live in Los Angeles, where I teach elementary school. I am planning to write more memoirs as well as some children's books on healthy eating.

Veronica Grix

P.S. Who are your heroes? Who are the heroes of your friends and relatives? Why? What does it mean to care about other people?

ABOUT THE ILLUSTRATOR...

Taylor Bruce was born and raised in the Pacific Northwest. Through the influence of artistic parents and her love of children's literature, she was inspired to pursue a career in children's book illustration. She attended San Francisco's Academy of Art College, where she received an award in the prestigious New York Society of Illustrators student competition. Upon graduation, Taylor moved to Sonoma County, California, to begin her career. *The Day Martin Luther King Jr. Died* is the tenth children's book she has illustrated.